It's another Quality Book from CGP

This book is for anyone doing GCSE Mathematics at Higher Level.

It's packed with questions — just like the ones you'll face in the real Exam. And they're all organised into topics — so after you've done a bit of revision, you can easily check whether you <u>really</u> understood it.

Remember... the key to getting better at Maths is practice — the more you practise, the better you'll get.

What CGP is all about

Our sole aim here at CGP is to produce the highest quality books — carefully written, immaculately presented and dangerously close to being funny.

Then we work our socks off to get them out to you — at the cheapest possible prices.

Contents

Published by Coordination Group Publications Ltd.

Contributors:

Cath Brown
Terence Brown
Tim Burne
Pamela Chatley
Jane Chow
Peter Clegg
Margaret Darlington
Michael Davidson
Angela Duffy
Christine Graham
Peter Hall
Hazel Harper
Tony Herbert
Paul Jordin
Simon Little
Alan Mason
Jeanette Whiteman

With thanks to Thomas Harte and Peter Caunter for the proofreading.

ISBN: 978 1 84146 589 0

Groovy website: www.cgpbooks.co.uk

Jolly bits of clipart from CorelDRAW®
Printed by Elanders Hindson Ltd, Newcastle upon Tyne

Types of Number

1 From the following list of numbers, find an example of each type of number below:

7   9   10   8   20

(a) A square number: ....   (b) A triangle number: ....

(c) A cube number: ....   (d) A prime number: ....

2 This question is about two special kinds of number.

(a) Find the sum of the first five square numbers. ....

....

(b) Find the product of the first five triangle numbers. ....

....

3 Place the following in order of size, starting with the smallest:

6^2 3^4 2^5 4^2 5^3

....

....

4 Which of the following numbers is prime?

2^3 15   29   51 3^2

....

5 Work out $2^3 \times 4^2$.

....

6 Find the value of x in each of the following:

(a) $2^x = 64$ ....

(b) $5^x = 125$ ....

(c) $3^x = 243$ ....

7 Circle TRUE or FALSE for each of the following statements:

(a) $3^2 = 2^3$ TRUE   FALSE   (b) $3^2 + 4^2 = 5^2$ TRUE   FALSE

2

Prime Numbers

1 List all the prime numbers between 40 and 60.

....

....

2 State all the prime numbers in the list below:

73   27   61   25   1   81

....

....

3 Find the product of the first five prime numbers.

....

....

4 Decide whether each of the following numbers is prime:

(a) 143 ....

....

(b) 257 ....

....

(c) 379 ....

....

5 If a and b are prime numbers, give an example to show that each of the following statements is **false**:

(a) $a + b$ is always even. ....

....

(b) $a \times b$ is always odd. ....

....

(c) $a^2 + b^2$ is always even. ....

....

Multiples, Factors and Prime Factors

1   From the numbers on the right, write down: **24**   **16**   **9**   **7**   **30**

   (a)   a multiple of 5 ....

   (b)   a factor of 36 ....

   (c)   a multiple of both 6 and 8 ....

2   This question is about multiples and factors.

   (a)   Write down the multiples of 6 between 40 and 50. ....

   (b)   Write down all the factors of 60. ....

....

3   Any positive whole number can be expressed as the product of its prime factors.

   (a)   Express 30 as a product of its prime factors. ....

....

   (b)   Express 36 as a product of its prime factors. ....

....

   (c)   Hence find the lowest common multiple (LCM) of 30 and 36. ....

....

4   The highest common factor (HCF) of two numbers is the largest number that divides into them both.

   (a)   Express 48 as a product of its prime factors. ....

....

   (b)   Express 108 as a product of its prime factors. ....

....

   (c)   Hence find the HCF of 48 and 108. ....

5   a and b are prime numbers.

   Find a and b if $a^4 \times b = 80$. ....

....

Fractions

1 Work out the following:

   (a) $\frac{1}{5}$ of £75.80 ....

   (b) $\frac{3}{8}$ of 60.8 m ....

2 Place the following quantities a, b and c in order of size, smallest first:

   $a = \frac{2}{3}$ of 120 $b = \frac{3}{4}$ of 80 $c = \frac{3}{5}$ of 70

....

....

3 Work out the following, giving your answers in their simplest form:

   (a) $\frac{2}{3} \times \frac{9}{10}$ ....

   (b) $3\frac{1}{7} \times 1\frac{1}{7}$ ....

4 Give your answers to the following in their simplest form:

   (a) $\frac{3}{8} \div \frac{9}{10}$ ....

   (b) $3\frac{1}{2} \div 1\frac{3}{4}$ ....

5 Find the area of a rectangle measuring $3\frac{4}{7}$ m by $1\frac{2}{5}$ m.

....

....

6 A fishing rod is $2\frac{1}{4}$ metres long.

How many equal sections of length $\frac{3}{8}$ metre can it be folded into?

....

....

7 If $a = \frac{3}{4}$ and $b = 2\frac{1}{2}$, find the value of $\frac{1}{a} + \frac{1}{b}$.

....

....

Fractions

1 Rewrite these fractions in order of size, smallest first:

$$\frac{7}{8} \qquad \frac{5}{6} \qquad \frac{3}{4} \qquad \frac{2}{3}$$

....

2 Find the values of *a*, *b*, *c* and *d* in the equations below:

$$\frac{a}{100} = \frac{12}{b} = \frac{c}{20} = \frac{45}{d} = \frac{3}{4} \qquad a = ...\qquad b = ...\qquad c = ...\qquad d = ...$$

3 If $a = 3\frac{1}{2}$ and $b = 2\frac{3}{5}$, work out:

(a) $a + b$ ....

(b) $a - b$ ....

4 Amy walked $\frac{2}{3}$ km to the bus stop. She then travelled $3\frac{2}{5}$ km by bus.
What was the total length of her journey?

....

5 A rectangular field measures $1\frac{3}{4}$ km by $\frac{7}{8}$ km. What is the perimeter of the field?

....

6 A bag and its contents weigh $2\frac{1}{2}$ kg. If the bag weighs $\frac{4}{5}$ kg, find the weight of the contents.

....

7 Add together the lengths in the box:

$$1\frac{1}{2} \text{ m}, \quad 50 \text{ cm}, \quad \frac{3}{4} \text{ m}, \quad 1 \text{ m } 45 \text{ cm}, \quad 1\frac{2}{5} \text{ m} \ \text{ and } \ 1.3 \text{ m}$$

....

....

....

Ratios

1   Mortar is to be made using cement, lime and sand in the ratio of 2:1:9.
    If 500 cm³ of cement is used, work out the amount of lime and sand needed.

    ....

    ....

    ....

2   In a class of 26 children, 12 are boys and the rest are girls.

    (a) What is the ratio of boys to girls? Give your answer in its simplest form.

    ....

    (b) One girl joins the class and two boys leave. What is the new ratio of boys to girls?

    ....

3   A stand is to be made from a plank of wood 238 cm long.
    It is cut into four pieces in the ratio 3:5:5:4. How long will each piece of wood be?

    ....

    ....

    ....

    ....

Ratios

1   Brothers Simon, Gareth and David invest some money and share any profit in the ratio 5:3:4.

   (a)   If Simon received £180, how much did Gareth receive?

   ....

   ....

   (b)   Next year the expected profit is £840. How much will each brother's share be?

   ....

   ....

2   Jane receives £10 pocket money per week.
   Sally receives £56 pocket money every four weeks.
   What is the ratio of Jane's pocket money to Sally's?

   ....

   ....

3   Green paint is made by mixing yellow and blue paint together in the ratio $3\frac{3}{4} : 1\frac{1}{2}$.

   (b)   Express this ratio in its simplest form.

   ....

   (b)   If 1355 ml of yellow paint is used, how much blue paint is needed?

   ....

4   A model of a new ship is made to a scale of 1:250.

   (a)   If the length of the model is 39 cm, calculate the length of the real ship in metres.

   ....

   (b)   Another ship is 87.5 m long.
   Calculate the length of its model in centimetres if it is made to the same scale as the first.

   ....

8

Percentages

1 Work out:

(a) 30% of £80 ....

(b) 15% of 600 m ....

2 A computer costs £900 plus VAT, where VAT is charged at 17½%.
   What is the total cost of the computer?

   ....

3 In a school 57 pupils out of 128 in Year 9 reach level 5 in their Science examination.
   Express this amount of pupils as a percentage.

   ....

4 After an 8% pay rise Mr Brown's salary was £15,500.
   What was his salary before the increase?

   ....

   ....

5 This is a question about percentage loss and percentage gain.

(a) Mr Jones buys a house for £80,000 and later sells it for £95,000.
    Calculate his percentage profit.

   ....

(b) Mrs Evans buys a car for £17,000 and later sells it for £14,500.
    Calculate her percentage loss.

   ....

Section One

Recurring Decimals and Surds

1   Write in the form $\frac{a}{b}$:

(a) $0.\dot{7}$ ....

(b) $0.\dot{2}\dot{6}$ ....

(c) $0.\dot{7}2\dot{9}$ ....

2   Circle TRUE or FALSE for each of the following statements:

(a) $\sqrt{32} = 4\sqrt{2}$ TRUE   FALSE   (b) $\sqrt{3}\sqrt{2} = \sqrt{6}$ TRUE   FALSE

(c) $\sqrt{4} + \sqrt{4} = \sqrt{8}$ TRUE   FALSE   (d) $(\sqrt{5})^2 = 5$ TRUE   FALSE

(e) $\frac{3}{\sqrt{3}} = \sqrt{3}$ TRUE   FALSE

3   Simplify the following as much as possible:

(a) $\sqrt{2} \times \sqrt{8}$ .... (b) $\sqrt{48}$ ....

(c) $\sqrt{100}$ .... (d) $5\sqrt{125}$ ....

(e) $\sqrt{27} + \sqrt{18}$ ....

4   Rationalising a denominator means making sure that there are no irrational numbers on the bottom line of a fraction.

(a) Simplify the following, making sure that the denominator is rational.

$\frac{2}{\sqrt{3}} \times \frac{3}{\sqrt{3}}$ ....

(b) Rationalise the denominator in these fractions:

(i) $\frac{3}{\sqrt{5}}$ ....

(ii) $\frac{5}{\sqrt{3}}$ ....

(iii) $\frac{7}{\sqrt{12}}$ ....

5 Answer these questions involving irrational products:

(a) Expand and simplify $(2 + \sqrt{3})(2 - \sqrt{3})$.

....

(b) Write $(2 + \sqrt{3})(5 - \sqrt{3})$ in the form $a + b\sqrt{3}$, where a and b are integers.

....

Rounding Numbers and Bounds

1 The distance between two stars is 428.6237 light years.

Round 428.6237:

428.6237 light years

   (a) to 2 decimal places   ....

   (b) to 2 significant figures ....

2 The height of a plant is 18 cm, to the nearest cm.
What is the least possible total height of 7 such plants?

....

3 A newspaper reported the number of people watching a tennis match as 15 000, correct to 2 significant figures.

Circle the numbers below which could round to 15 000, to 2 significant figures.

15 624	14 820	15 200	14 499	14 599

4 The length of a patio is advertised as being, *'16 m to the nearest ½ metre'*.

   (a) What is the smallest it could be?

....

   (b) What is the biggest it could be?

....

5 The following details have been recorded at a county show.
Complete the table to show the least and greatest possible amounts for each item.

Item	Measure	Least possible	Greatest possible
orange squash	250 cl, to 2 sig. fig.		
a prize onion	22 oz, to the nearest oz		
a courgette	23.8 cm, to the nearest mm		

Rounding Numbers and Bounds

1   Bags of sand weigh 32 kg, to the nearest kg. What is the maximum weight of 8 bags of sand?

    ....

2   The time to run 100 m was recorded as 12.5 s, to the nearest 0.1 s.
     State the upper and lower bounds of this time.

    ....

3   If $a = 2.8$ and $b = 3.6$ (both correct to 1 decimal place), find:

    (a) The maximum possible value of $a + b$ ....

    ....

    (b) The minimum possible value of $b - a$ ....

    ....

    (c) The maximum possible value of ab ....

    ....

    (d) The minimum possible value of $\dfrac{a}{b}$ ....

    ....

4   The table shows the heights of the highest
     mountains in Scotland, Wales and England.

Mountain	Height (metres)
Ben Nevis	1344
Snowdon	1086
Scafell Pike	979

    (a) How high is Ben Nevis to the nearest thousand metres?

    ....

    (b) How high is Snowdon to the nearest hundred metres? ....

    (c) Round the height of Scafell Pike to:

        (i)   the nearest hundred metres.

        ....

        (ii) the nearest ten metres.   ....

Accuracy and Estimating

1   Decide the appropriate accuracy for each of these measurements in the situation described, and round them off accordingly:

(a)   A golfer trying to decide how high a tree is.

The exact height of the tree is 48.75 m.   ....

(b)   The club doctor wanting to know the weight of a footballer.

The footballer's exact weight is 78.2543 kg.   ....

(c)   A businessman wanting to know his average speed for a motorway journey.

His exact average speed was 69.593 mph.   ....

2   Place these numbers in order of size, smallest first:

$$\sqrt{79} \qquad 8.5 \qquad \sqrt{60} \qquad 7.5 \qquad \sqrt{50}$$

....

3   Estimate each of the following to 1 decimal place:

(a) $\sqrt{23}$ ....   (b) $\sqrt{38}$ ....

(c) $\sqrt{95}$ ....

4   Estimate the value of $\dfrac{523 + 694}{17.9 + 2.13}$, showing all your working.

....

....

5   The formula for the total surface area of a closed cylinder is $A = 2\pi r^2 + 2\pi rh$.
Estimate the surface area of a cylinder of base radius 1.89 cm and height 5.92 cm.

....

....

6   Estimate the size of these everyday objects:

(a)   the volume of a family saloon car (in m³) ....

....

(b)   the area of the palm of your hand (in cm²) ....

....

Arithmetic

1 Without using a calculator, answer the following:

    (a) 21.29 + 16.07 =

....

    (b) 11.3 + 13.42 =

....

    (c) 48.34 – 17.95 =

....

    (d) 29.66 – 14.7 =

....

2   Without using a calculator, answer the following:

    (a) $19 \times 3.5 =$

....

    (b) $2.3 \times 12 =$

....

    (c) $6.6 \times 1.7 =$

....

3   Without using a calculator, answer the following:

    (a) $217 \div 3.1 =$

....

    (b) $234 \div 1.8 =$

....

    (c) $5390 \div 2.45 =$

....

14

Conversion Factors, Metric and Imperial Units

1 Put these lengths in order of size, smallest first:

   600 cm   2 yards   8 feet   3.6 m   70 inches

   ....

2 Circle TRUE or FALSE for each of the following statements:

   (a) 5 kg < 10 lbs   TRUE   FALSE

   (b) 8 litres > 2 gallons   TRUE   FALSE

   (c) 6.5 inches is approximately equal to 16.25 cm   TRUE   FALSE

   (d) 500 g < 1 lb   TRUE   FALSE

3 Mr Birchall travelled from London to Glasgow. He measured his journey as 400 miles. What is this distance in kilometres?

   ....

4 The petrol tank of Mrs Pardoe's car holds 20 gallons. How many litres is this?

   ....

5 A horse averaged a speed of 20 km per hour in a race. What is this speed in:

   (a) metres per second?

   ....

   (b) miles per hour?

   ....

6 The exchange rate is given as £1 = 1.65 US dollars.

   (a) Change £300 to US dollars. ....

   (b) Convert 80 US dollars to pounds. ....

7 A map is drawn to a scale of 2 cm to 1 km.

   (a) Work out the real length of a field which measures 5.6 cm on the map.

   ....

   (b) The distance between two towns is 7.5 km. What is this distance on the map?

   ....

Section One

Finding the nth Term

1   A sequence begins: **1, 6, 11, 16, ...**

   (a)   What are the next two terms?

   .... and ....

   (b)   Write down the first two terms bigger than 100.

   .... and ....

   (c)   What is the *n*th term of this sequence?

   ....

2   This question is about a number sequence.

   (a)   Write down the next 2 terms in this sequence:

   3   4   7   11   ☐   ☐

   (b)   Explain how the pattern continues.

   ....

3   Fill in the gaps in the following sequences:

   (a)   ☐   **6   12   24   48**   ☐

   (b)   ☐   **3   7   12**   ☐   **25**   ☐

4   The *n*th term of a sequence is given by $u_n = 3n + 2$.

   (a)   What are the first 3 terms of this sequence?

   ....

   (b)   Which term is equal to 101?

   ....

Finding the nth Term

1   A sequence of numbers is shown below.

   4, 9, 14, 19,...

   (a) Find the *n*th term. ....

   (b) What is the 20th term? ....

   (c) Which term has the value 209? ....

2   This question is also about sequences.

   (a) Write down the next two terms in the sequence 3, 7, 11, 15,... ....

   (b) Find the *n*th term of the sequence. ....

   (c) Show that 502 cannot be a term in this sequence. ....

   (d) Calculate the number of terms in the sequence 3, 7, 11, 15,…, 199. ....

   ....

3   Not all sequences increase by the same amount each time.

   (a) Write down the next two terms in the sequence 3, 8, 15, 24,... ....

   (b) Find the *n*th term of the sequence. ....

   ....

   (c) What is the 30th term of the sequence? ....

4.   The positive integers can be arranged as shown opposite:

   The sequence of numbers 1, 3, 6, 10, 15,…
   is formed by the last number in each row.

```
              1
          2       3
       4      5       6
    7      8      9      10
 11    12     13     14     15
```

   (a) What is the name of this sequence of numbers? ....

   (b) Write down the next 3 numbers in the sequence. ....

   (c) Find the *n*th term of this sequence. ....

   ....

   (d) What is the 20th number in the sequence? ....

   (e) Which term in the sequence has the value 820? ....

   ....

Numbers Mini-Exam (1)

1 Answer these questions without using a calculator:

(a) Work out $\frac{3}{5}$ of 16. ....

(b) Write down the value of $\sqrt{25} + 8^{\frac{2}{3}}$. ....

(c) Write down the value of $8^0 + 0.3^2$. ....

(d) Find an approximate value of $\frac{4.75}{18.4 + 1.9}$. ....

2 $n = 0.\dot{2}7\dot{8}$

(a) Write down the value of $1000n$. ....

(b) Hence express n as a fraction in its simplest form. ....

....

3 Jayne has received a bonus from work of £75 and wants to share it with her brother Karl. She decides to divide the money in the ratio of their ages. Jayne is 10 years old and Karl is 5 years old. How much money will Karl receive?

....

....

....

4 Last year Amy was 80 cm tall and weighed 25 kg.

(a) She is now 5% taller. Calculate her height now.

....

(b) Amy weighs 30 kg now. Calculate her percentage increase in weight.

....

5 The mass of a metal statue is 36 kg.

The density of the metal alloy from which it is made is 12 g/cm³.

(a) Calculate the volume of the statue.

....

It is decided that the metal alloy used is not resistant enough to wear and tear and is replaced with another that has a density of 17 g/cm³. The volume of the statue must remain the same.

(b) Calculate the mass of the new statue.

....

Numbers Mini-Exam (1)

6 From the list on the right, write down any: √25   61   9   15 2^3 2

(a) prime numbers ....

(b) multiples of 3 ....

(c) triangle numbers ....

(d) square numbers ....

(e) factors of 30 ....

7 Here, HCF stands for highest common factor, and LCM stands for lowest common multiple.

(a) Express 48 as a product of its prime factors. ....

(b) Express 72 as a product of its prime factors. ....

(c) Work out the HCF of 48 and 72. ....

(d) Work out the LCM of 48 and 72. ....

8 A garden has an area of 500 m², of which 60% is lawn. One quarter of the rest is patio.
What is the area of the patio?

....

....

9 Estimate the value of this fraction, showing all your working: $\dfrac{215.7 \times 48.8}{460}$

....

....

10 A restaurant orders 40 litres of milk. 75 pints are delivered instead.
Does the restaurant have enough milk? Show your working.

....

11 For each of the following, write down the value of x:

(a) $x^3 = 216$ ....

(b) $2^x = 64$ ....

(c) $5^x = 1$ ....

(d) $2^3 \times 4^x = 512$ ....

Numbers Mini-Exam (2)

1   Answer the questions that follow.

   (a) Write $2\frac{1}{4}$ as a decimal: ....

   (b) Place the following numbers in order of size, smallest first:

$$2\frac{1}{4} \qquad 1.29^2 \qquad 2.36 \qquad 2.14 \qquad \sqrt{4.65}$$

....

2   In France a car can be bought for 30,000 euros. In America the same car can be bought for 35,000 US dollars. The exchange rates for France and America are shown below.

   France: £1 = 1.45 euros   America: £1 = $1.67

   In which country is the car cheaper and by how much? Show all your working.

....

....

3   Write down the *n*th term and the 20th term of each of the following sequences:

   (a) 5   9   13   17   21 ....

....

   (b) 6   14   24   36   50 ....

....

4   When things become worth less as they get older, they are said to depreciate.

   (a) A caravan cost £18,500 when it was new. It is now worth £12,600.
        Calculate the percentage decrease in value. ....

   (b) Another caravan has dropped 30% in value. It is now worth £8,500.
        What was its original value? ....

5   A garage is 4.6 m long and 3.2 m wide, both correct to the nearest 0.1 m.
   The height of the garage is 9 feet 3 inches, correct to the nearest 3 inches.
   Assume there are 2.5 cm to one inch.
   Find the maximum possible volume of space occupied by the garage in m³.

....

....

Numbers Mini-Exam (2)

6   An athlete ran 100 m in 9.92 seconds. Calculate his average speed in kilometres per hour, giving your answer to a suitable degree of accuracy.

....

....

....

7   This question is about using formulas.

(a) If $s = ut + \frac{1}{2}at^2$, calculate s when $u = 5$, $t = \frac{3}{2}$, and $a = \frac{3}{4}$.

....

(b) The formula $F = \frac{9}{5}C + 32$ is used to convert temperatures in degrees Celsius (C) to temperatures in degrees Fahrenheit (F). A thermometer reads 36 °C.

What is this temperature in degrees Fahrenheit?

....

8   Claire goes on holiday. She changes £300 into euros. (Exchange rate is £1 = 1.45 euros.)

(a) How many euros does Claire receive? ....

(b) She spends $\frac{3}{4}$ of her money on food. How many euros is this?

....

(c) She spends 20% of the rest of her money on presents. How many euros is this?

....

9   There are 225 pupils in a school. Of these 105 are boys.

(a) What fraction of the pupils are boys? Give your answer in its simplest form.

....

(b) Emma goes on a charity walk of 200 miles. If she can average 12½ miles per day, how many days will it take her to complete the journey?

....

10   The square numbers form a special number sequence.

(a) What is the 5th square number?

....

(b) What is the 15th square number?

....

Regular Polygons

1 The regular pentagon drawn below has been extended to form angle *r*.

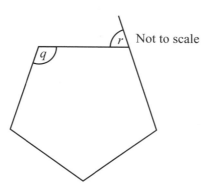

Not to scale

(a) Work out the size of angle *q*.

....

....

(b) Work out the size of angle *r*.

....

....

2 Calculate the size of the interior angle of a regular polygon with:

(a) 9 sides

....

(b) 15 sides

....

3 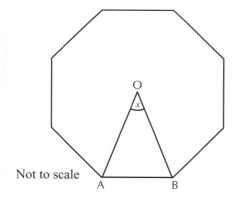 A sketch of a regular octagon is shown below.

(a) Work out the size of angle *x*.

....

....

....

Not to scale

A   B

(b) What type of triangle is OAB?

....

4 A regular polygon has an interior angle of 150°.
How many sides does the polygon have?

....

....

....

Symmetry

1 Mark all the lines of symmetry on the following shapes:

(a)

(b)

(c)

2 Identify the order of rotational symmetry for each shape below:

(a)

(b)

(c)

....

3 How many planes of symmetry do the following solids have?

(a) a cuboid

(b) a square-based pyramid

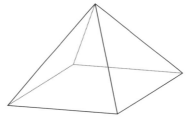

....

4 By shading in the smallest number of squares possible, complete the pattern on the right so that it has exactly two **axes** of symmetry.

Perimeters and Areas

1 Kylie uses a piece of string to measure the perimeter of shapes.
The string fits exactly round a rectangle 10 cm by 8 cm.

She then fits it exactly round a square.

How long is one side of the square?

....

2 The length of a rectangle is 8 cm.

The perimeter of the rectangle is 28 cm.

Calculate the width of the rectangle.

....

....

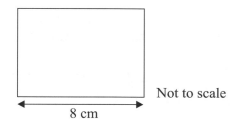

Not to scale

8 cm

3 The diagram below shows a triangle ABC.
The base BC = 12.5 cm. The perpendicular height AX = 8 cm.

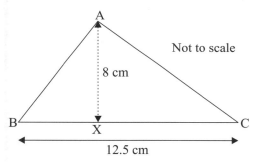

Not to scale

8 cm

12.5 cm

Calculate the area of the triangle.

....

....

4 Calculate the total area of the shape below.

30 cm

21 cm

9 cm   9 cm

6 cm   6 cm

Not to scale

....

....

....

Perimeters and Areas

1   A trapezium with an area of 168 cm² has parallel sides of lengths 6 cm and 18 cm.
How far apart are the parallel sides?

....

....

2   The diagram below shows the cross-section of a swimming pool.

   (a) Calculate the area of the cross-section shown. ....

....

   (b) Calculate the perimeter of the cross-section shown. ....

....

3   The diagram below shows the front elevation of a building.

Calculate the area of the front elevation of the building.

....

....

....

....

4   The area of the parallelogram shown below is 105 cm².

   (a) Calculate the height of the parallelogram.

....

....

....

   (b) Calculate the perimeter of the parallelogram.

....

....

Perimeters and Areas

1   A circular pond has an area of 40 m². Find the radius of the pond.

....

....

2   The diagram below shows a rectangular garden area with semicircle sections at either end, one for a flowerbed and the other for a patio area. The rest is lawn.

10 m

Not to scale

30 m

(a) Calculate the area of the lawn.

....

(b) Calculate the perimeter of the lawn.

....

3   The circle shown below has a radius of 12 cm and the sector subtends an angle of 50° at its centre.

50°

12 cm

Not to scale

Find the area of the sector of the circle.

....

....

....

....

4   Look at the sector in the diagram below.

Not to scale

30°

6 cm

Find the perimeter of the sector.

....

....

....

....

Surface Area

1 A tin of soup is in the shape of a cylinder. It has a radius of 3 cm and its height is 12 cm. The tin has a label which fits exactly around the cylinder with no overlap.

Calculate the area of the label. (Give your answer to 3 significant figures.)

....

....

2 Tins of ham are packed in a box for distribution.

The diagram below shows the dimensions of the box.

Using a scale of 1 cm: 6 cm, draw an accurate scale drawing of a net for this box.

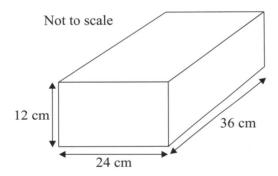

Not to scale

12 cm

36 cm

24 cm

3 The surface area of a cube is 150 cm².

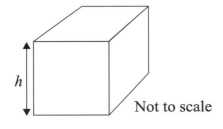

Calculate its height, h.

....

....

....

h

Not to scale

....

Volume

1 The cross-sectional area of a hexagonal prism is 15 cm².

Its height is 6 cm.

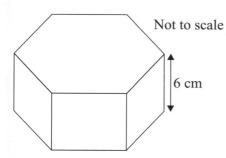

Not to scale

6 cm

Calculate the volume of the prism.

....

....

2 A cylindrical barrel of oil has a height of 1.5 m and a diameter of 0.6 m.

Calculate its total capacity.
(Give your answer correct to 2 decimal places.)

....

....

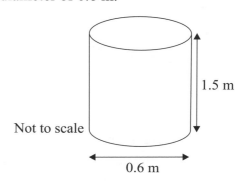

1.5 m

Not to scale

0.6 m

3 A single box of fudge has a volume of 480 cm³.

What is the maximum number of boxes of fudge that can be packed into a packing case with the following dimensions: length 48 cm, width 40 cm and height 16 cm?
(Assume the boxes can be packed into the case without leaving any gaps.)

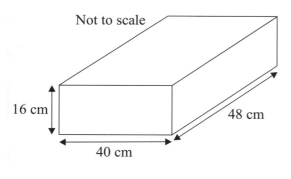

Not to scale

16 cm

48 cm

40 cm

....

....

Volume

1 A diagram of a storage tunnel is shown below.

24 m

Not to scale

←—12 m—→

Find the volume, correct to 3 significant figures.

....

....

....

....

2 A cricket ball has a diameter of 75 mm.
Calculate its volume in cubic centimetres.

....

....

....

3 A pyramid has a square base with 8 cm sides, and sloping edges 10 cm in length.
Find the volume of the pyramid.

....

....

....

4 The volume of the cone shown below is 113 cm³ correct to 3 significant figures.

Not to scale

12 cm

Calculate the radius of the cone.

....

....

....

Geometry

1 Find the marked angles on the diagrams below.

A = ...

B = ...

C = ...

D = ...

2 Triangle ABC is isosceles.

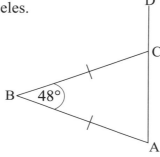

If ∠ABC = 48°, what is the size of ∠BCD?

....

....

3 Using the information in the diagram, find ∠BCD.

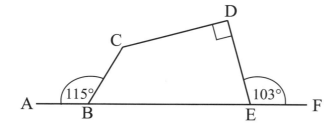

....

....

Geometry

1 The diagram below shows two lines intersecting two parallel lines.

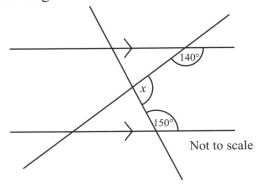

140°

x

150°

Not to scale

Find the size of angle *x*.

....

....

....

....

2 Look at the triangle shown below:

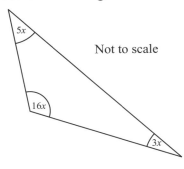

5x

Not to scale

16x

3x

Find the size of each of the angles in the triangle.

....

....

....

....

3 Look at the diagram below.

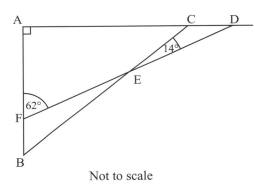

A   C   D

14°

E

62°

F

B

Not to scale

Calculate the following angles:

(a)   CDE

....

(b)   ACB

....

(c)   EBF

....

4 Look at the trapezium below.

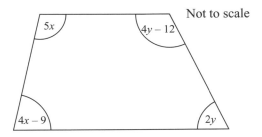

5x

4y – 12

Not to scale

4x – 9

2y

Calculate the values of *x* and *y*.

....

....

....

....

Circle Geometry

1 This diagram shows a circle with diameter AC.

Not to scale

(a) (i) Angles ADB and ACB are in the same segment.
What can you say about these angles?

....

(ii) What is angle ABC? Explain your answer.

....

....

(iii) Explain why $x = 28°$.

....

....

(b) If AD = BD, find y.

....

....

2 The diagram shows two circles with centres X and Y.
The straight lines ABC and EDC are tangents to both circles.
Angle ACE = 32°.

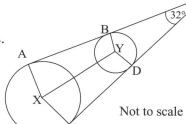

Not to scale

(a) Explain why AB = ED.

....

....

....

(b) (i) Write down the size of angles CBY and CDY. ....

(ii) Hence calculate the size of angle BYD.

....

(iii) Angles BYX and DYX are equal. How big are they? ....

(iv) Write down the size of angle XAB. ....

(v) Hence find angle AXY.

....

Circle Geometry

1 This diagram shows a circle with centre O. A, B and C are points on the circumference and angle BOC is 150°.

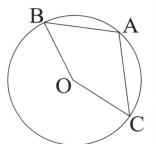

Not to scale

(a) (i) How big is the reflex angle BOC?

....

(ii) Explain why angle BAC = 105°.

....

(b) The lengths of AB and OA are equal.

(i) What can you say about triangle OBA? What is angle OBA?

....

(ii) What is angle OCA?

....

(iii) Calculate angle BCO.

....

(iv) Hence find angle BCA.

....

2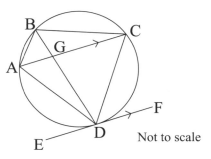

Not to scale

In the diagram on the left, the line EF is a tangent to the circle and is parallel to the chord AC.

Angle EDA = 71° and angle BAD = 100°.

(a) Write down the size of angle ACD.

....

(b) ABCD is a cyclic quadrilateral.

(i) Find the size of angle BCD. ....

(ii) Hence, show that angle BCA = 9°. ....

(c) Find the following angles, giving a reason for each answer:

Angle DAG ....

Angle ADC ....

Angle CDF ....

Angle BDA ....

Angle BDC ....

Loci and Constructions

1 The following is a scale drawing of Akela Troop scoutfield.
The council agree that the scouts can have a bonfire subject to two conditions:
  1. The bonfire must be the same distance from Stroll Lane as from Amble Road.
  2. It must be equidistant from the electricity pylons at P and Q.

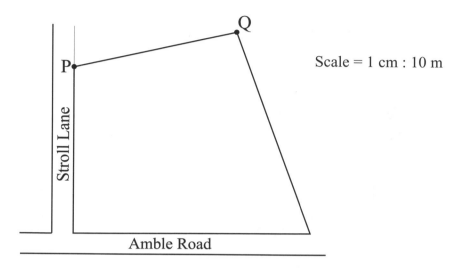

Scale = 1 cm : 10 m

Use a ruler and compasses to find and mark clearly the position of the bonfire.

2 The diagram is a scale map of the road running due north from Alchester to Burbridge.

(a) Corway is due east of Burbridge and on a bearing of 060° from Alchester.
    Using a ruler and compasses only, find and mark Corway on the map.

Scale = 1 : 50 000

(b) A straight canal runs from Alchester to Corway.
    A landing stage is to be built on the canal where it runs closest to Burbridge.
    Draw and measure the length of the straight path from Burbridge to the landing stage.

Loci and Constructions

Use a ruler and a pair of compasses to answer the questions on this page:

1   A fountain is to be placed in the park shown below. It must be closer to point C than B.
It must also be closer to point A than C.
Shade in the region where the fountain may be placed.

2   A dog is tied to a wire AB by a lead which allows it to run a maximum of 2 m from the wire.
Shade the region on the diagram where the dog may run, using the scale shown.

AB

Scale: 1 cm represents 1 m

3   Construct an equilateral triangle.
From one of its corners, draw a line that is perpendicular to the opposite side.

Transformations

1 Triangle ABC has been drawn on the grid below.

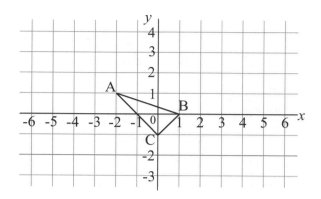

(a) Enlarge ABC by a factor of 3 about the origin. Label the image $A_1B_1C_1$.

(b) Enlarge $A_1B_1C_1$ by a factor of 0.5 about the centre (-6, -1). Label the image $A_2B_2C_2$.

(c) Describe the transformation which will map ABC directly onto $A_2B_2C_2$.

....

2 The shaded triangle has an area of 3 cm².

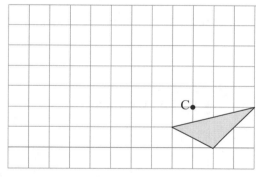

Each small square = 1 cm²

(a) Enlarge the triangle by a factor of –2 about the point C.

(b) Calculate the area of the image.

....

....

3 A spherical iron cannonball 8 cm wide weighs 2.4 kg.
A similar spherical cannonball made of the same material weighs 12 kg. Find its width.

....

....

....

....

Transformations

1 A, B and C are images of the shaded shape on the grid below.

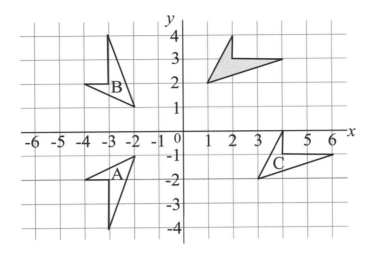

(a) Describe the transformation which will map the shaded shape onto:

(i) A ....

(ii) B ....

(iii) C ....

(b) Describe the single transformation for which C is the image of B.

....

2 An L shape has been drawn on the grid on the right.

(a) Draw the image when this shape is:

(i) reflected in the *x*-axis.
Label this image A.

(ii) rotated through 90° anticlockwise
about the point (-1, 0).
Label this image B.

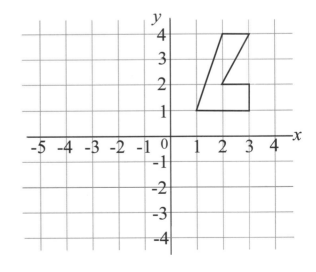

(b) What single transformation will map A onto B?

....

Projections, Congruence and Similarity

1 Look at the shapes below. You might find tracing paper useful for this question.
Which shapes are:

(a) (i) congruent to Shape A? .... (ii) similar to Shape A? ....

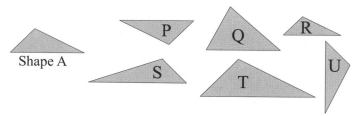

(b) (i) congruent to Shape B? .... (ii) similar to Shape B? ....

2 Sketch and label the elevations of each solid viewed in the direction of the arrows.

(a)

(b)

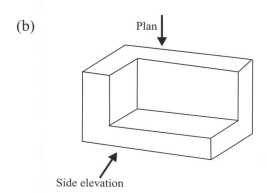

Shapes and Area Mini-Exam (1)

1 In the diagram FAE is a tangent to the circle.
FBGD and CGA are straight lines. AD = CD.

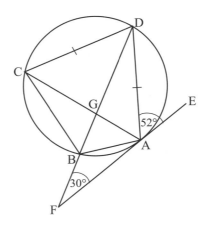

Not to scale

(a) Find angle ADC.

....

(b) Find angle FDA.

....

(c) Find angle ACB.

....

(d) Find angle BGC.

....

2 Triangle PQR has been drawn on this grid:

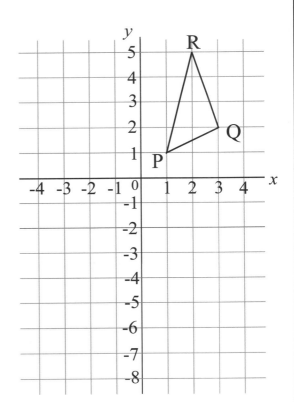

(a) Reflect PQR in the line $y = -1$.
Label the image $P_1Q_1R_1$.

(b) Reflect $P_1Q_1R_1$ in the line $y = x - 4$.
Label the image $P_2Q_2R_2$.

(c) Describe the transformation for which
PQR is the image of $P_2Q_2R_2$.

....

....

Shapes and Area Mini-Exam (1)

3 The diagram represents three isosceles triangles.
This is because AB = AC, and BC = BD = AD.
Angle BCA = $x°$.

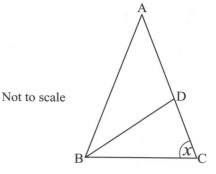

Not to scale

(a) Angle BAD can be expressed in terms of x as $3x - 180$. By looking at triangle ABC, write down a **different** expression for angle BAD in terms of x.

....

(b) Form an equation, and hence find x.

....

4 In this diagram AB and CD are parallel.

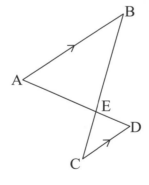

Not to scale

(a) Show that triangles ABE and DCE are similar.

....

....

(b) Given that AB = 18 cm, CD = 6 cm, CE = 5 cm and AD = 16 cm, find the lengths of:

(i) BE ....

(ii) DE ....

(c) Describe how you could transform triangle CDE onto BAE.

....

Shapes and Area Mini-Exam (2)

1   Below is a scale plan of a goat G tethered by a 5 m rope to a shed in the corner of a large field. The goat cannot go inside the shed.

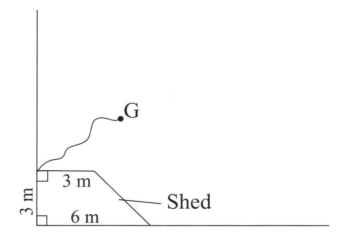

(a) Draw and shade the locus where the goat can graze.

(b) Find the area of this region.

....

....

2   The frustum shown on the right was cut from a cone.

Not to scale

(a) Explain why the original cone must have been 15 cm high.

....

....

(b) Find the volume of the frustum. (Volume of a cone = $\frac{1}{3}\pi r^2 h$)

....

....

....

(c) What percentage of the original cone was discarded?

....

....

Shapes and Area Mini-Exam (2)

3   Each angle of a regular polygon is 168°.
    How many sides does the polygon have?

    ....

    ....

4   This diagram represents a rectangular room.

(a) Find its surface area.

    ....

    ....

(b) Sketch a net of the cuboid.

(c) A spider is at S, and a fly at F. Points S and F are midway along their respective edges.
     Mark S and F on your net and hence find the shortest distance for the spider to get to the fly
     along the walls of the room.

    ....

    ....

    ....

Pythagoras' Theorem

1   A ladder of length 2.5 m is lent against a vertical wall. The top of the ladder is 2 m from the ground. How far is the bottom of the ladder away from the bottom of the wall?

   ....

   ....

2   A triangle has a base of 10 cm. Its other two sides are both 13 cm long. Calculate the perpendicular height of the triangle.

   ....

   ....

Not to scale

13 cm   13 cm

10 cm

3   Point A has coordinates (2, 1).
   Point B has coordinates (11, 13).
   How many units long is the line segment joining A to B?

   ....

   ....

   ....

4   The diagram shows a kite ABCD. AB is 5.83 units long.
   BC is 9.43 units long.
   BE is 5 units in length.
   How long to the nearest unit is AC?

   ....

   ....

   ....

   ....

   ....

   ....

   ....

A   Not to scale

5.83

D   E   5   B

9.43

C

Bearings

1 A boat is in distress. The coastguard sees the boat on a bearing of 110° from point C.
The lighthouse keeper sees the boat on a bearing of 045° from point L.
On the diagram below, mark the position of the boat. Label the position B.

N

C.
Coastguard

L.
Lighthouse

2 The diagram shows an orienteering course. Competitors start from A and run to B.
The scale of the diagram is 2 cm to 1 km.

.B

N

.A

(a) What is the bearing of B from A?

....

(b) C is 2 km away from B on a bearing of 240°. Mark and label the position of C on the
diagram.

3 Mount Adam is on a bearing of 065° from Mount Billy and 320° from Mount Cuthbert.
Mark the position of Mount Adam on the diagram and label it A.

N

Mount.
Billy

. Mount
Cuthbert

Trigonometry

 1 Find the angles marked *x* in the following triangles. (Give your answers to 1 decimal place.)

(a)

(b)

(c)

....

 2 Find the sides marked *y* in the following triangles.
(Give your answers to 3 significant figures.)

(a)

(b)

(c)

....

 3 In the triangle below, AB = BC = 10 m and angle C = 34°.

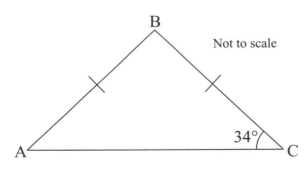

$\cos 34° = 0.829$
$\tan 34° = 0.675$
$\sin 34° = 0.559$

(a) Calculate AC.

....

(b) Calculate the altitude of the triangle.

....

Section Three

Trigonometry

1 The diagram EFGH shows a kite.

Diagonal EG bisects diagonal HF at M.

EM = 5 cm, MG = 9 cm and HF = 12 cm.

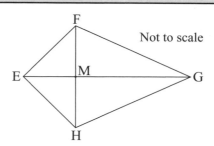

(a) Calculate angle FGM. ....

(b) Calculate angle FEH. ....

2 A cliff is 125 m high.

From the top of the cliff, the angles of depression of two boats, both due east, are 16° and 23° respectively.

Calculate the distance between the boats. (Give your answer to 3 significant figures.)

....

....

3 A boy at point P, on one edge of a straight stretch of river, observes two posts, Q and R, on the opposite bank. Q is directly across from P, and the distance between Q and R is 60 m.

River   Not to scale

The boy estimates the angle QPR to be 40°.

Calculate the width of the river.

....

4 A regular hexagon is drawn such that all of its vertices are on the circumference of a circle of radius 8.5 cm.

Calculate the distance from the centre of the circle to the centre of one edge of the hexagon. (Give your answer to 2 decimal places.)

....

The Sine Rule

1 In the following triangles calculate the missing sides or angles marked *x*:

(a)

(b)

(c)

....

2 The diagram below is a functional sketch of a metal framework with some of the manufacturing information missing.

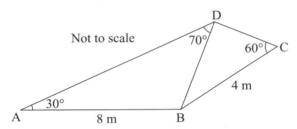

In the triangular frame BCD, calculate:

(a) BD ....

(b) Angle BDC ....

(c) DC ....

3 Two ships P and Q are positioned such that Q is 8 km from P on a bearing of 100° from P.

A third ship R is on a bearing of 160° from P and 200° from Q.

(a) Draw a sketch of this information and clearly mark the ships P, Q and R.

(b) Calculate PR. ....

(c) Calculate QR. ....

The Cosine Rule

1 In the triangle, calculate the angles marked *x* and *y*. (Give your answers to 1 decimal place.)

....

....

2 In the triangle to the right, calculate (AC)².

....

....

....

3 The diagram below shows a circular clock face with centre O. The hands OA and OB are 12 cm and 10 cm long respectively.

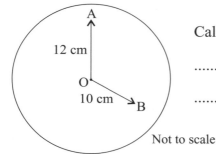

Calculate the shortest distance between A and B at 4 pm.

....

....

4 A, B and C are three landmarks on level ground.

A is 8 km due north of B. C is to the west of AB. The distance AC is 6.5 km and BC is 5 km.

(a) Draw a sketch diagram to show this information.

(b) Calculate the angle BAC. ....

(c) State the bearing of C from A. ....

Vectors

1 Three vectors are defined as:

$$\underline{l} = \begin{pmatrix} 4 \\ 2 \end{pmatrix} \qquad \underline{m} = \begin{pmatrix} -3 \\ 2 \end{pmatrix} \qquad \underline{n} = \begin{pmatrix} 1 \\ -4 \end{pmatrix}$$

Evaluate the following:

(a) $\underline{l} + \underline{m}$ ....

(b) $3\underline{m} - \underline{n}$ ....

(c) $2\underline{l} + \underline{m} - 2\underline{n}$ ....

2 In the diagram on the right, *ABCD* is a parallelogram.

L is the midpoint of AC, and M is the midpoint of BC.

Write in terms of $\underline{a}$ and $\underline{d}$:

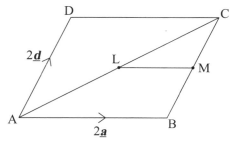

(a) **CD** ....

(b) **AC** ....

(c) **LM** ....

(d) **BL** ....

3 Look at the diagram on the right.

(a) Write in terms of $\underline{x}$ and $\underline{y}$:

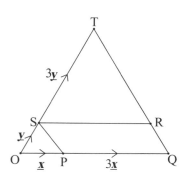

(i) **SP** ....

(ii) **TQ** ....

(b) Prove that SP is parallel to TQ.

....

....

Sin, Cos and Tan Graphs

1 The graph below shows $y = \sin x$ for values of x between $0°$ and $360°$.

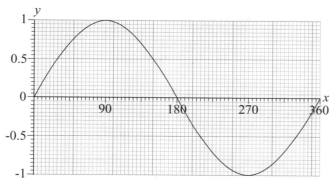

(a) Using the graph and your calculator, find all the angles between $0°$ and $360°$ that satisfy:

(i) $\sin x = 0.5$

(ii) $\sin x = -0.9$

(iii) $4\sin x = 1.37$

(b) Complete the following table:

x	0	45	90	135	180	225	270	315	360
$\cos x$	1			-0.71	-1		0		1

(c) Plot the graph of $y = \cos x$ on the grid above and find the angles between $0°$ and $360°$ that satisfy the equation: $\sin x = \cos x$.

2 Indicate whether the following statements are true or false:

(a) $\cos 65°$ is positive.

(b) $\tan 100°$ is positive.

(c) $\sin 250°$ is negative.

(d) $\cos 330°$ is negative.

3 Which of the following values cannot be the sine of an angle?

0.5, 1, -0.65, 0.866, 1.2, 0.32, -1.4

Trigonometry Mostly Mini-Exam (1)

1 The graph of $y = f(x)$ is shown on the grids below.

(a) On this grid sketch the graph of

$y = f(x)+2$

(b) On this grid sketch the graph of

$y = f(x/2)$

2 Two ships leave Dover at the same time.

Ship A travels due south for 40 km. Ship B travels 60 km on a bearing of 140°.

(a) Using a scale of 1 cm = 10 km, draw the journeys of the two ships in the space below and clearly mark their final positions.

N
↑
Dover ●

(b) (i) Measure the final bearing of Ship B from Ship A.

....

(ii) Hence, calculate the final bearing of Ship A from Ship B.

....

Trigonometry Mostly Mini-Exam (1)

3 The graph below represents $y = \cos x$.

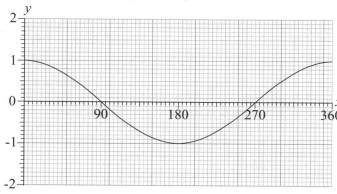

(a) Using the graph, find all the angles between 0° and 360° that satisfy the following equations:

(i) $\cos x = 0.5$

....

(ii) $\cos x = -0.2$

....

(iii) $5 \cos x = 4$

....

(b) Use what you know about the symmetry of sin x to complete the table below.

x	0	45	90	135	180	225	270	315	360
$2 \sin x$	0		2	1.4				-1.4	0

(i) Plot $y = 2 \sin x$ on the same axes as the graph of $y = \cos x$ (above).

(ii) Use your graph to find all the angles between 0° and 360° that satisfy: $\cos x = 2 \sin x$

....

4 In the diagram on the right, ABC is an equilateral triangle, with side length 20 cm. M is the midpoint of AC and O is the centre of the inscribed circle.

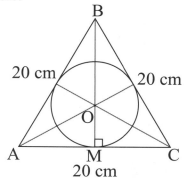

Angle (°)	Sin	Cos	Tan
30	0.5	0.866	0.577
60	0.866	0.5	1.732

Using the trigonometric values above, calculate to 3 significant figures:

(a) The altitude of the triangle (BM).

....

(b) The diameter of the inscribed circle.

....

Trigonometry Mostly Mini-Exam (2)

1 A sea kayaker paddles between an island and the mainland. He paddles on a bearing of 035°, heading initially for point Y. The tide is moving Westwards at 2 knots. He eventually reaches the mainland at point X, directly North of his starting point.

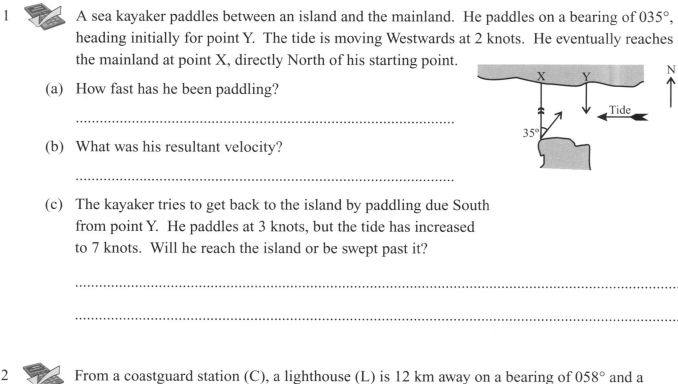

(a) How fast has he been paddling?

....

(b) What was his resultant velocity?

....

(c) The kayaker tries to get back to the island by paddling due South from point Y. He paddles at 3 knots, but the tide has increased to 7 knots. Will he reach the island or be swept past it?

....

....

2 From a coastguard station (C), a lighthouse (L) is 12 km away on a bearing of 058° and a buoy (B) is 8 km away on a bearing of 135°.

(a) Draw a sketch diagram of this information.

(b) Calculate the distance of the lighthouse from the buoy.
(Give your answer to 2 decimal places.)

....

3 This question is about angles between 0° and 360°.

(a) Find the two solutions to the equation: $\sin x = 0.423$

....

(b) Find the smallest possible value of p which satisfies the equation: $\cos p = \cos 210°$.

....

Trigonometry Mostly Mini-Exam (2)

4 The sketch below is of the graph of $y = x^2$. Sketch the following graphs on the axes.

(a) $y = 2x^2$

(b) $y = (x + 3)^2$

(c) $y = x^2 - 2$

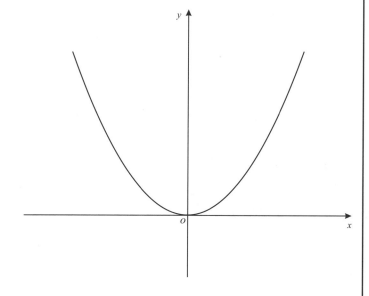

5 A hot-air balloon is 25 m from the ground and 40 m from its landing spot.
Work out the angle of depression of the landing spot from the hot-air balloon.

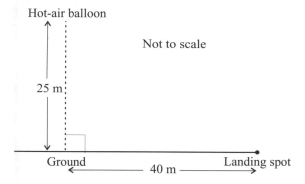

....

....

....

....

....

6 The cuboid ABCDEFGH shown below is an insect trap.

AB = 20 cm, BC = 10 cm and AE = 5 cm.

A beetle and a wasp are caught at point A and decide to try and escape from point G.
The beetle chooses the route A to C to G.
The wasp chooses the direct route A to G.

Calculate the distances of the two different routes.

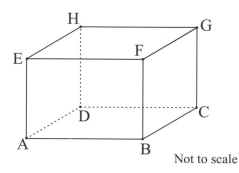

Not to scale

....

....

....

D/T and V/T Graphs

1 An object is projected vertically upwards. Its distance/time graph is shown below.

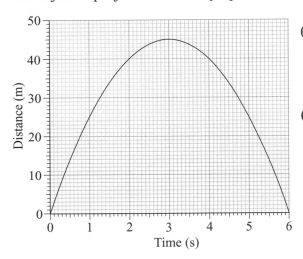

(a) At what time is the object momentarily at rest?

....

(b) By drawing a tangent, estimate the velocity of the object at time $t = 2$ seconds.

....

....

2 The velocity/time graph below shows the details of one qualifying lap, driven by James Sprint, in the Outer Mongolian Grand Prix.

(a) What is his average acceleration during the 15 to 30 second period?
(State the units for your answer.)

....

(b) What is the meaning of the negative gradient at the end of the lap?

....

(c) What is the length of one lap?

....

Coordinates

1 Point P has coordinates (6, 5) and point Q has coordinates (2, -1).

Find the length of PQ, giving your answer correct to two decimal places.

....

....

2 Point A has coordinates (2, 5, 7).

Point B has coordinates (0, 3, 8).

Point C has coordinates (3, 7, 5).

(a) Find the lengths of lines AB and AC.

....

....

(b) What can you say about triangle ABC?

....

3 Point P has coordinates (6, 2) and point Q has coordinates (-4, 1).

(a) Find the coordinates of the midpoint of PQ.

....

....

Point R has coordinates (a, b).

(b) The midpoint of PR is (3, 5).

Find the values of a and b.

....

....

Straight Line Graphs

1 Draw and label the following graphs on the axes below:

$y = -1$

$x = 0$

$x = 2$

$y = x$

$y = -2x$

2 The box below contains the equations of some lines and curves.

Tick the ones that are equations of straight lines.

$x + y = 0$	$y = 2x^2$	$y = \frac{1}{2}x - 2$
$xy = 8$	$x = 2$	$2y + 3x = 2$
$y^2 + x^3 = 2$	$y = \dfrac{x}{3}$	$y = \dfrac{3}{x}$

3 Draw and label these graphs on the axes below:

$2y + x = 7$

$y = 2x + 3$

Straight Line Graphs

1 This question is about straight line graphs.

  (a) Find the gradient and the y-intercept for each of the following straight line graphs:

    (i) $y = 3x + 2$

    ....

    (ii) $y = 5 - x$

    ....

    (iii) $2x + y = 7$

    ....

    (iv) $x - 5y - 2 = 0$

    ....

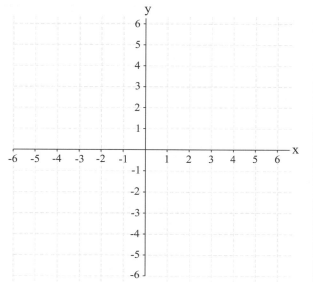

  (b) Use your answers to parts (i) and (ii) above to sketch the graphs of $y = 3x + 2$ and $y = 5 - x$.

2 Match the lines A, B, C and D in the diagram to the equations below:

$y = 4 + x$ ......

$x + y = 6$ ......

$y = 2x$ ......

$3y - x = 2$ ......

3 Look at the straight line graph shown in the diagram.

  (a) Find the equation of the straight line graph.

  ....

  (b) A straight line graph has the same gradient as the one in part (a), but goes through the point (0, -1).

    (i) Write down the equation of this graph.

    ....

    (ii) Sketch the graph on the axes on the right.

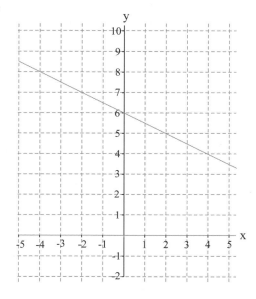

Solving Equations Using Graphs

1   A ball is thrown upwards from the top of a cliff, so that it falls down to the sea below.

The cliff is 50 m high.

The graph shows the height *h* of the ball from sea level, *t* seconds after it has been thrown.

From the graph, find:

(a) the time taken for the ball to fall to sea level.

....

(b) the height of the ball after 4 seconds.

....

(c) the time when the ball is again at the same height as the cliff.

....

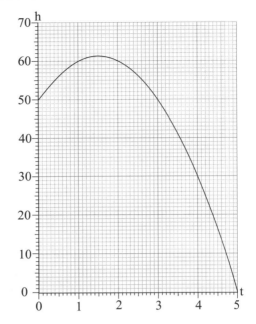

(d) the maximum height of the ball above the ground, and the time at which it reaches this height.

....

2   This question is about the function $y = x^3 - 4x^2 + 4$.

(a) Complete the table below. The first few have been done for you.

x	-1	-0.5	0	0.5	1	1.5	2	2.5	3	3.5	4
$x^3 - 4x^2 + 4$	-1	2.875	4	3.125	1	-1.625	-4				

(b) Use your table to draw the graph of $y = x^3 - 4x^2 + 4$ on the axes on the right.

(c) Using your graph or otherwise, estimate:

(i) the value of *y* when *x* = 3.2.

....

(ii) the value(s) of *x* when *y* = 0.

....

....

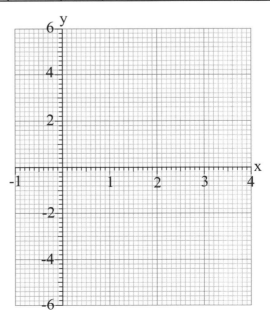

Simultaneous Equations and Graphs

1. The diagram shows part of the graph of $y = 4x - x^2$.

   (a) Using the same axes, draw the graph of $y = 5x - 2$.

   (b) Use the graphs to find the solution(s) to the simultaneous equations:

   $y = 5x - 2$

   $y = 4x - x^2$

   ....

2. On the axes below, draw suitable graphs and hence obtain the solution of the simultaneous equations:

   $4y + 3x = 25$

   $2y - x = 5$

   ....

   ....

3. The diagram shows the graphs of $y = \dfrac{6}{x-2}$ and $y = 2x - 5$.

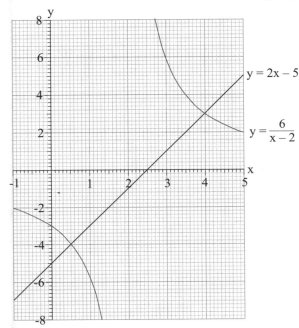

   Using these graphs, write down the solution(s) of the equation:

   $6 = (x - 2)(2x - 5)$

   ....

Finding Equations from Graphs

1 The graph on the right is of the form $y = a - bx^2$.

(a) Write down the coordinates of the points where the graph crosses:

(i) the x-axis. ....

(ii) the y-axis. ....

(b) Hence find the equation of the curve.

....

2 Bilal had to learn the stopping distances of a car at various speeds for his driving theory test.

Instead of learning a table of values, he thought it would be easier to find a formula for them.

He drew this graph from his table of values.

Bilal thought the graph was of the form $d = av + bv^2$.

Find the values of a and b.

....

3 Look at the diagram below.

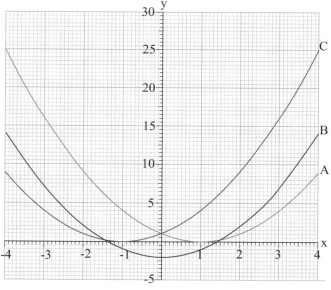

Each of these graphs can be obtained from the graph of $y = x^2$ by a single translation.

(a) Describe the translation for each graph.

....

....

....

....

....

(b) Use your answers to (a) to give the equation of each graph.

....

Finding Equations from Graphs

1 The diagram below shows the graph of $y = ax^3 + b$.

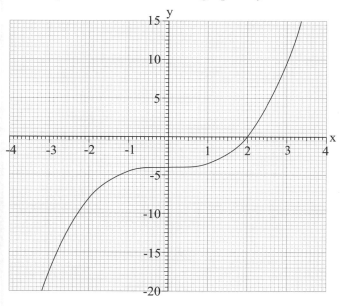

Find the values of a and b.

....

2 The diagram on the right shows the graph of $y = ax^3 - bx^2 + c$.

(a) Explain why $c = 3$.

....

....

(b) Use the point $(1, 4)$ to show that $a - b = 1$.

....

(c) Use the point $(-1, 0)$ to find another equation connecting a and b.

....

(d) Find the values of a and b.

....

....

Graphs Mini-Exam (1)

1 There are two taxi firms in Anytown. The two firms work out their charges as shown below:

Tel's Taxis: £1 basic fee + 20p per 100 metres

Kev's Kabs: No basic fee, but 30p per 100 metres

(a) Draw and label lines to represent these charges on the axes below.

(b) Explain what is represented by:

(i) the gradient of the lines.

....

....

(ii) the intercept on the *y*-axis.

....

....

(c) Use your graph to find the distance for which the two companies charge the same.

....

(d) Someone asks your advice on which taxi firm to use. Write down what you would tell them.

....

2 The diagram below shows the curve $y = x^2$.

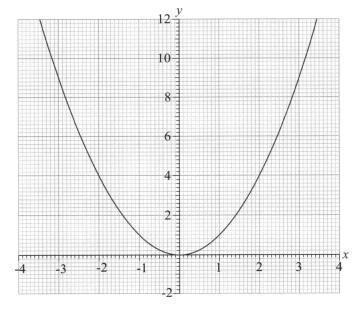

(a) On the same axes, draw the curve $y = (x - 2)^2$.

(b) Use your graphs to write down the point at which $x^2 = (x - 2)^2$.

....

Look at the gradient of $y = x^2$ at the point $(1, 1)$.

(c) Find the coordinates of a point on $y = (x - 2)^2$ where the curve has the same gradient.

....

Graphs Mini-Exam (1)

3 A printing firm quotes these figures for printing different numbers of leaflets:

Number of leaflets	100	200	500	1000	2000	5000
Price per leaflet	£1	50p	20p	10p	5p	2p

(a) Plot these points on the axes below and draw a smooth curve through them.

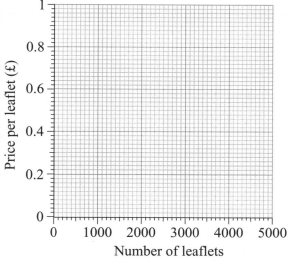

(b) Use your graph to work out the likely cost per leaflet for 2500 leaflets.

....

(c) The curve you have drawn has the equation $P = \dfrac{k}{N}$, where P = price in pounds per leaflet, and N = number of leaflets. Find the value of k.

....

....

4 A donkey and a mule set out on a 1 km race. The donkey runs at 24 km/h, but every 400 m it stops for 5 min to eat a carrot. The mule keeps going at 5 km/h.

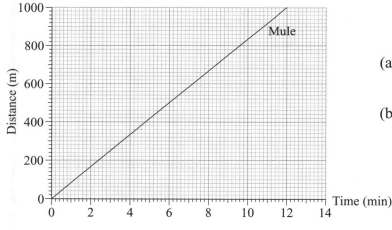

The graph on the left shows the mule's race.

(a) Plot the graph for the donkey's race on the same axes.

(b) Who wins the race and by how many seconds?

....

....

(c) After how many minutes into the race does the mule first overtake the donkey?

....

Graphs Mini-Exam (2)

1 Answer the question below about the graph of $y = x^3 - 2x^2 + x + 1$.

(a) Complete the table of values:

x	-3	-2	-1	0	1	2	3
x^3							
$-2x^2$							

(b) Using your table to help you, draw the graph of $y = x^3 - 2x^2 + x + 1$ on the axes below.

(c) Use your graph to find the value(s) of x for which $y = -5$.

....

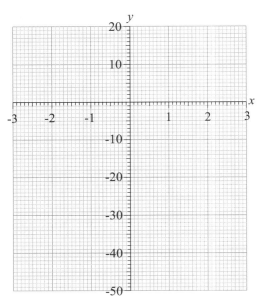

2 Points P and Q are plotted on graph paper.

Point P is (3, 7). Point Q is (2, 9).

(a) Find:

(i) the length of PQ (give your answer to 2 decimal places).

....

(ii) the midpoint of PQ. ....

(b) Find the gradient of PQ. ....

(c) If the line PQ is extended, it goes through the point R, with coordinates (0, c).

(i) What is the gradient of QR?

....

(ii) Use your answers to (b) and (c) (i) to find c.

....

(d) Write down the equation of the line that goes through P and Q.

....

Graphs Mini-Exam (2)

3   The diagram below shows a straight line.

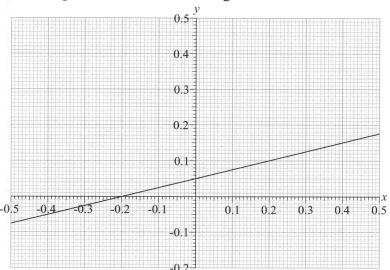

(a)   Find the equation of the line.

....

....

(b)   On the same axes, draw the line $2x + y = 0.5$.

(c)   Write down:

(i)   the intersection point of these two lines. ....

(ii)   a pair of simultaneous equations to which this point gives the solution.

....

4   Sanjay did a physics experiment on pendulums. He took pendulums of various lengths, and noted the time it took for each pendulum to complete a full swing backwards and forwards. Here are his results:

Length (L) / metres	0.2	0.4	0.6	0.8	1.0	1.2	1.4	1.6	1.8	2.0
Time (T) / seconds	0.90	1.27	1.55	1.80	2.01	2.20	2.37	2.54	2.69	2.84

(a)   Plot these points on the graph paper below and connect them with a smooth curve.

(b)   Use your graph to find:

(i)   the length of a pendulum that takes 1.1 seconds for a full swing backwards and forwards.

....

(ii)   the time a pendulum of length 0.9 m takes for a full swing backwards and forwards.

....

Sanjay thinks that this curve is of the form $T = a\sqrt{L}$.

(c)   Find a.

....

Probability

1 There are four blue counters and six red counters in a bag. One counter is picked out at random. Write the probabilities of the following events as fractions in their lowest terms.

(a) A blue counter is picked out. ....

(b) The counter picked out is not blue. ....

(c) A green counter is picked out. ....

(d) The counter picked out is red or blue. ....

2 I am thinking of a number. It is either one or two. P(1) = 0.4. What is P(2)? ....

3 A four-sided spinner (which can show 1, 2, 3 or 4) is deliberately made unfair. P(x) represents the probability of getting x when the spinner is spun.

P(1) = 0.1, P(2) = 0.3, P(3) = 0.5.

(a) Work out P(4) ....

(b) What is P(1 or 2)? ....

(c) What is P(odd number)? ....

(d) What is P(number greater than 1)? ....

4 A fair six-sided dice is thrown once.

(a) What is P(3)? ....

(b) What is P(even number)? ....

5 There are ten counters in a bag. Seven are green and all the rest are yellow. One counter is picked out but is not replaced. A second counter is then picked out.

(a) Complete the following tree diagram.

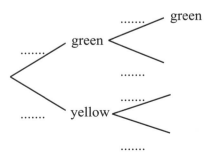

(b) What is the probability that both counters chosen are yellow? ....

(c) What is the probability that both counters chosen are green? ....

(d) What is the probability that both counters chosen are different colours? ....

Probability

1 Sanjay has two fair dice numbered 1–6. He throws them together and adds the scores.

Calculate:

(a) P(a score of 7) ....

(b) P(a total of more than 8) ....

2 Here is a 5-sided spinner. The sides are labelled 1, 2, 3, 4 and 5.
The spinner is biased. The probability that the spinner will
land on the numbers 1 to 4 is given in this table.

Number	1	2	3	4	5
Probability	0.3	0.15	0.2	0.25	

(a) Work out the probability the spinner will land on an odd number.

....

(b) I spin the spinner twice. Work out the probability that I will score 3 both times.

....

3 A box of chocolates contains 12 chocolates. 5 of the chocolates are milk chocolate,
4 are plain chocolate and 3 are white chocolate. I choose 2 chocolates at random.

1st chocolate	2nd chocolate	Outcomes

$$\begin{array}{lll} & \text{Milk} \dotfill & \text{MM} \\ \text{Milk} <\!\!\!\!\!\!\!\text{.......} \text{Plain} & & \text{MP} \\ & \text{White} \dotfill & \dotfill \end{array}$$

1st chocolate: Milk $\frac{5}{12}$, Plain $\frac{4}{12}$, White $\frac{3}{12}$

2nd chocolate from Milk: Milk ...., Plain ...., White .... → MM, MP, ...

2nd chocolate from Plain: Milk ...., Plain ...., White .... → ...., ..., ...

2nd chocolate from White: Milk ...., Plain ...., White .... → ...., ..., ...

By completing the tree diagram above, calculate the probability that I pick:

(a) one milk and one white chocolate.

....

(b) at least one plain chocolate.

....

Mean, Median, Mode and Range

1. For Susan's GCSE statistics project she asked 10 pupils in her class for their shoe sizes.
   These are her results:

   $$5, 6, 8, 7\frac{1}{2}, 5, 3, 6, 6, 4, 7$$

   (a) For this set of data write down:

   (i) the mode ....

   (ii) the median ....

   (iii) the range ....

   (iv) the mean ....

   (b) Susan decides to include her own shoe size in the data,
   which increases the mean shoe size to 6.

   Calculate:

   (i) Susan's shoe size.

   ....

   (ii) the mode, median and range now.

   ....

   ....

2. There are 15 boys and 13 girls in a class. In a Maths test the mean mark for the boys was b.
   In the same test the mean mark for the girls was g.
   Write down an expression for the mean mark of all 28 pupils.

   ....

   ....

3. I am thinking of 3 numbers.

   The mean of my numbers is 22.

   The range of my numbers is 31.

   The median number is 29.

   Write down my 3 numbers.

   ....

   ....

   ....

Frequency Tables

1 The table shows the number of pets owned by each pupil in class 7F.

Number of pets	0	1	2	3	4	5
Frequency	8	3	5	8	4	1

(a) How many pupils are there in class 7F?

....

(b) What is the mean number of pets per pupil?

....

2 For her GCSE homework Vanessa collected information about the number of text messages pupils in her school sent each day. She recorded her results in the frequency table below.

Number of messages	0	2	3	5	7	8	10
Frequency	2	5	8	6	5	2	1
Number × frequency			24			16	

(a) Complete the frequency table.

(b) Use the table to calculate:

(i) the mean number of text messages sent.

....

....

(ii) the modal number of text messages sent.

....

....

(iii) the median number of text messages sent.

....

....

Grouped Frequency Tables

1 32 pupils in a class sat an exam in Science.
The distribution of their marks is given in the table below.

Exam mark	$10 < x \leq 20$	$20 < x \leq 30$	$30 < x \leq 40$	$40 < x \leq 50$	$50 < x \leq 60$	$60 < x \leq 70$
Frequency	2	5	7	8	4	6
Mid-interval value						
Frequency × mid-interval value						

(a) Complete the table.

(b) Use the table to find:

(i) the modal group. ....

(ii) the group which contains the median.

....

(iii) an estimate of the mean (give your answer to 1 decimal place).

....

2 During a science experiment 10 seeds were planted and their growth measured in cm
after 12 days. The results were recorded in the table below.

Growth in cm	0-2	3-5	6-8	9-11
Number of plants	2	4	3	1

Use the table to find:

(a) the group which contains the median.

....

(b) the modal class.

....

(c) an estimate of the mean.

....

(d) Explain why you can only find an "estimate".

....

....

Cumulative Frequency

1 120 pupils in a year group sit an examination at the end of the year.
Their results are given in the table below.

Exam mark (%)	$0 < x \le 20$	$20 < x \le 30$	$30 < x \le 40$	$40 < x \le 50$	$50 < x \le 60$	$60 < x \le 70$	$70 < x \le 80$	$80 < x \le 100$
Frequency	3	10	12	24	42	16	9	4

(a) Complete the cumulative frequency table below and use it to
draw a cumulative frequency curve on the graph paper.

Exam mark (%)	≤20	≤30	≤40	≤50	≤60	≤70	≤80	≤100
Cumulative Frequency								

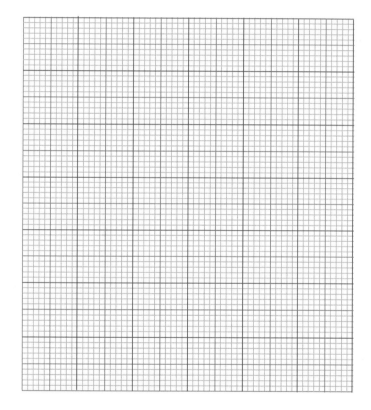

Use your curve to find:

(b) (i) The median mark ....

(ii) The lower quartile ....

(iii) The upper quartile ....

(iv) The inter-quartile range ....

(c) Use your results from part (b) to draw a box plot to illustrate the data.

Histograms and Frequency Density

1 The scores of individual pupils in an exam are given below:

$$75, 52, 50, 73, 58, 50, 61, 55, 43, 45, 65$$

(a) Draw a stem and leaf diagram for this data.

(b) Find the range of the results from your diagram.

....

2 The histogram shows the number of minutes pupils watch television for one evening.

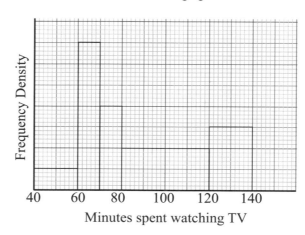

Minutes spent watching TV

20 pupils watched between 40 and 60 minutes.

(a) Use the histogram to complete this table.

Number of minutes watched	Frequency
$40 \le m < 60$	20
$60 \le m < 70$	
$70 \le m < 80$	
$80 \le m < 120$	
$120 \le m < 140$	

(b) How many pupils took part in the survey?

....

Correlation, Dispersion and Spread

1 What type of correlation would you expect to see if you drew a scatter graph to compare:

(a) the age of a car and its value? ....

(b) hand span and index finger length? ....

(c) shoe size and number of pets? ....

2 As part of his GCSE project work, Sam decided to ask 10 primary school pupils how old they were and what time they were sent to bed. He recorded his results in the table below.

Age in years	6	9	9	6	8	7	9	7	8	8
Bedtime	7.30	8.15	8.30	7.00	8.00	7.30	8.45	8.00	8.15	7.45

(a) Draw a scatter graph to show this information.

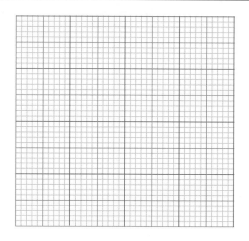

(b) Sam's little brother is 6½ years old. According to your graph, what time should he expect to go to bed? ....

3 A simple test of 10 maths questions was given to all pupils moving to a secondary school. A bar chart of the results is shown below.

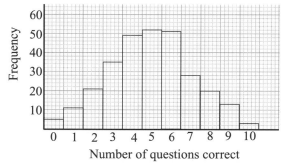

(a) Comment on the shape of the distribution.

....

(b) Estimate the value of the mean.

....

Other Graphs and Charts

1 Each student in a class of 30 owns one pet, as shown in the table below.

Type of Animal	Dog	Cat	Goldfish	Snake	Rabbit
Frequency	15	5	3	2	5

Draw a pie chart to represent this information.

2 The grouped frequency table below shows the number of hours of homework 30 students did in one week.

Hours of Homework	0 to 2	2 to 4	4 to 6	6 to 8
Frequency	15	7	5	3

Draw a frequency polygon for the data.

3 This two-way table shows the number of adults and the number of children living in houses on Avenue Road:

		Number of Adults				
		1	2	3	4	Total
Number of Children	0	1	1	1	1	
	1	2	2	1	0	
	2	2	5	0	0	
	3	0	2	0	0	
	4	0	1	0	0	
	Total					

(a) Complete the table to show the totals for each of the rows and columns.

(b) How many houses had 2 adults and 3 children living in them? ....

(c) How many houses had 2 children living in them? ....

(d) How many houses were there on Avenue Road? ....

Sampling Methods and Time Series

1   Susie is investigating the heights of pupils in her school in order to advise the company that make the school uniform. There are 720 pupils in the school.

Year	7	8	9	10	11
Number of pupils	167	162	150	125	116

(a) Describe:

(i)   how a random sample of 100 students could be chosen.

....

....

(ii) how a stratified random sample of 100 students could be chosen, stating how many students would come from each year group.

....

....

....

....

(b) What additional information would she need in order to carry out a quota sample?

....

2   A new football club wants to see if there is any trend in its attendance figures.

Week	1	2	3	4	5	6	7	8	9	10
Members	32	25	43	28	42	32	44	46	30	45

(a) Calculate the four-weekly moving averages.

....

....

....

(b) Describe the trend you can see in the attendance figures.

....

....

Handling Data Mini-Exam (1)

1 The stem and leaf diagram shows the amount of rainfall in mm that fell during a period of 14 days one November.

Key:	1	2 = 12 mm

```
0 | 1  2  2  3  4
1 | 2  3  5  5
2 | 0  2  2  2  3
```

(a) Write down the modal value. ....

(b) Write down the median value. ....

(c) Calculate the range of the data. ....

(d) Calculate the mean value. ....

....

2 200 pupils sat an entrance exam. The cumulative frequency curve shows the marks they obtained.

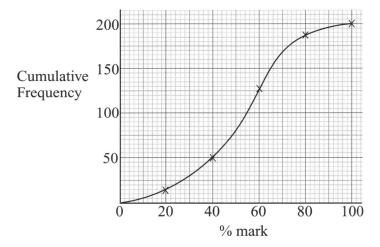

Use the graph to find:

(a) (i) the median mark. ....

(ii) the lower quartile. ....

(iii) the upper quartile. ....

(iv) the inter-quartile range. ....

(b) If the pass mark was 64 marks, estimate how many pupils passed.

....

Handling Data Mini-Exam (1)

3 In a particular class in school 15 pupils study both Spanish and Italian.
Their end of year exam results are given in the table below.

Spanish (%)	42	32	61	41	53	72	65	50	80	43	66	38	23	12	72
Italian (%)	54	43	70	44	60	76	72	62	91	52	71	42	38	24	81

(a) Draw a scatter diagram to illustrate this data.

(b) Describe the correlation you can see in your diagram. ....

(c) Ahmed was absent for his Spanish exam but scored 66% for his Italian.
Estimate the mark he might have obtained for Spanish. ....

4 A school contains 800 pupils.
The number of pupils in each year group is given in the table below.

Year	7	8	9	10	11
Number of pupils	184	160	136	176	144

A stratified sample of 100 pupils is to be taken. How many pupils should be picked from each year group?

....

....

....

Handling Data Mini-Exam (2)

1 The weekly wages of 70 part-time workers at a factory are given in the table.

Wages (£)	Number of employees
70 – 79	3
80 – 89	11
90 – 99	8
100 – 109	15
110 – 119	24
120 – 129	7
130 – 139	2

(a) Use the table to write down:

(i) the group containing the modal wage. ....

(ii) the group that contains the median wage.

....

(b) Calculate an estimate of the mean wage.

....

....

2 On my way to work in the morning the probability that I stop to buy a newspaper is 0.7.
If I stop to buy the paper the probability that I am late for work is 0.4.
On other mornings the probability that I am late for work is 0.15.

(a) Complete the tree diagram to illustrate this situation.

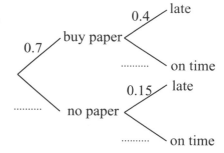

(b) Use the tree diagram to calculate:

(i) the probability that I am on time for work and I have bought a newspaper.

....

(ii) the probability that I am late for work.

....

(c) If I am at work for 200 days a year, how many days can I expect to be late?

....

Handling Data Mini-Exam (2)

3 The temperature in London was recorded for 15 days one July.
The highest daily temperature was recorded and the results are given below.

Day	1	2	3	4	5	6	7	8	9	10	11	12	13	14	15
Temp (°C)	28	26	24	27	19	22	23	23	21	20	17	19	25	25	24

(a) Draw a box plot of this data, marking clearly the value of the median and the lower and upper quartiles.

(b) Calculate the mean of the data.

....

....

4 The histogram shows the weight of apples which fell from a tree.
There were 8 apples in the 30-50 g group.

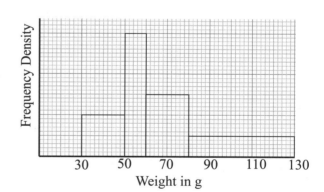

Use the histogram to find the total number of apples which fell.

....

....

5 During bad weather, the probability that I have an accident in my car on a given day is $\frac{1}{40}$.

In fine weather this reduces to $\frac{1}{200}$. The probability of bad weather on any day is $\frac{1}{5}$.

Calculate P(I have a car accident on a given day).

....

....

Powers and Roots

1 Evaluate the following and list them in order of size, starting with the smallest:

3^0 $\qquad$ $4^{1/2}$ $\qquad$ 5^{-3} $\qquad$ $8^{4/3}$ $\qquad$ $9^{-1.5}$ $\qquad$ $\left(\dfrac{2}{3}\right)^3$

....

2 Simplify the following:

(a) $a^5 \times a^{-3}$

....

(b) $\dfrac{x^7}{x}$

....

(c) $\dfrac{(d^3)^2}{d^4}$

....

(d) $\dfrac{(b^2)^4}{b \times b^6}$

....

3 Solve the following equations:

(a) $2^x = 32$

....

(b) $10^x = 1/100$

....

(c) $9^x = \sqrt{9}$

....

(d) $3^x = (3^4)^2 \times \dfrac{3^5}{3^{11}}$

....

Compound Growth and Decay

1. During the first hour of an 8-hour shift, a machine produces 480 bolts.

    (a) If the production rate drops by 10% every hour, how many bolts will be produced in the second hour?

    ....

    (b) How many bolts will be produced in the last hour of the shift?

    ....

    ....

2. Answer the following questions about exponential growth and decay:

    (a) The population of fish in a lake is estimated to decrease by 8% every year.
    How many will be left after 15 years if the initial population is 2000?

    ....

    ....

    (b) A new house cost £120 000, but increased in value by 15% each year.
    Work out its value after 5 years, to the nearest £1000.

    ....

    ....

    (c) The speed of a toy car running around a track falls by 10% every lap.
    If the speed on the first lap is 4 m/s, how fast will it be travelling on the sixth lap?

    ....

    ....

3. If interest is added to an account at the end of each year, work out how many years it takes to double your money for each of the following rates of interest:

    (a) An interest rate of 5% per annum. ....

    ....

    (b) An interest rate of 9% per annum. ....

    ....

Basic Algebra

1 Complete the diagram by writing expressions in the empty boxes:

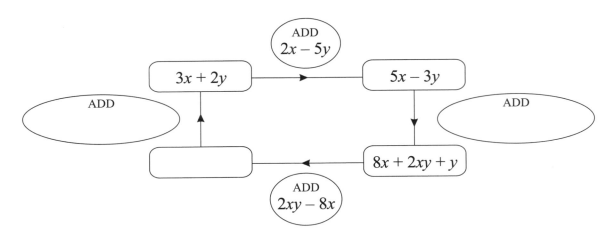

2 Write **one** term in each empty space to make the equation correct:

(a) $2(3x + 5) = 6x +$ ....

(b) ....$(4a -$ ....$) = 12a^2 - 6a$

(c) $3x -$ .... $+ 4(2x + 5) =$ ....$+ 18$

(d) $6($ .... $- 4) - (d -$ ....$) = 17d - 22$

3 Multiply out the brackets in these expressions. Simplify your answers as much as possible.

(a) $5x - 3(x - 1)$ ....

(b) $4a(b + 1) + b(2a - 1)$ ....

(c) $8(3 - 2p) - 2(p - 3)$ ....

(d) $(2t - 5)(3t + 4)$ ....

(e) $(x + 3)^2$ ....

Basic Algebra

1 Write a term in each empty space to complete the factorisations below:

(a) $8b - 12 =$ ....$(2b -$ ....$)$

(b) $2a^2 +$ .... $= 2a($ .... $+ 3b)$

(c) $9d^2e -$ .... $+ 15de^2f = 3de($ .... $- e^2 +$ ....$)$

(d) .... $- 16 = (x -$ ....$)(x +$ ....$)$

2 Factorise the following three expressions as much as possible:

(a) $15x^2 - 6xy =$ .... $($..$)$

(b) $12x^2 + 10x =$ .... $($..$)$

(c) $8x - 12xy =$ .... $($..$)$

3 Simplify the following as much as possible:

(a) $\dfrac{4a \times 3ab}{6ab^2}$

....

....

(b) $\dfrac{10x}{3+x} \div \dfrac{4}{5(3+x)}$

....

....

(c) $\dfrac{2}{3} + \dfrac{m - 2n}{m + 3n}$

....

....

(d) $\dfrac{y^2 - 1}{3y + 3}$

....

....

Standard Index Form

1   Standard form is used to express very large and very small numbers.

   (a) Express the following numbers in standard form:

       (i)   12500 ....

       (ii) 0.0064 ....

       (iii) 8.6 ....

   (b) A and B are two numbers in standard form:

       $A = 4.834 \times 10^9$, $B = 2.417 \times 10^5$

       (i) Express A and B as ordinary numbers.

            ....

       (ii) Evaluate $A \div B$. (Give your answer in standard form.)

            ....

2   Light travels at approximately 1.86×10^5 miles per second. Calculate the following:
    (Give your answers in standard form to 3 significant figures. State the units of your answers.)

   (a) What distance will light travel in one year (365 days)?

       ....

   (b) The distance from the Earth to the Sun is approximately 9.3×10^7 miles.

       How long will it take light to travel this distance?

       ....

3   An average grain of sand has a mass of 4.2×10^{-4} g and a volume of 8.3×10^{-2} mm^3.

    Answer the following questions, giving your answers to the nearest grain.

   (a) How many grains of sand would have a combined mass of 1 gram?

       ....

   (b) How many grains of sand will it take to fill 1 cm^3?

       ....

Solving Equations

1. Solve the equations below:

   (a) $x + 3 = 12$

   (b) $2y - 5 = 9$

   (c) $3z + 2 = z + 15$

   (d) $12 - 3x = 17$

2. Find the solution to the following equations:

   (a) $3(a + 2) = 15$

   (b) $2b - 7 = 2(3b + 1) - 29$

   (c) $5(2c - 1) = 4(3c - 2)$

3. Solve these equations:

   (a) $\dfrac{4 - 3d}{5d} + 7 = 6$

   (b) $\sqrt{2(3h + 5)} = 5$

   (c) $3x^2 = 12$

Solving Equations

1 This is a question about finding unknown values in equations.

Solve these equations:

(a) $2p + 3 = 12$ ....

(b) $17 - 3q = q + 4$ ....

(c) $2r - 6 = 3(3 - r)$ ....

(d) $s^2 - 19 = 17$ ....

2 Solve the following linear equation:

$7y - (10 - y) = 3(y - 1) + 4y - 2.5$ ....

....

3 Work through the steps to <u>find the solution</u> to this equation:

$$\sqrt{5 + \frac{(8x - 7)}{(5 - 2x)}} = 2$$

(a) Square both sides to get: ....

(b) Multiply throughout by $(5 - 2x)$ to get: ....

(c) Expand the brackets to get: ....

(d) Collect like terms on each side of the equation to get: ....

(e) Solve the linear equation to find x: ....

4 Solve:

(a) $\sqrt{\dfrac{1}{x}} = 4$ ....

(b) $\dfrac{(x + 3)}{2} + \dfrac{(x - 5)}{4} = 10$ ....

....

5 Find the value of m which satisfies this equation:

$\dfrac{5}{m - 1} = \dfrac{5}{7 - m}$ ....

Rearranging Formulas

1 Follow the instructions given for each equation below:

   (a) Collect the terms with y in on the left-hand side of the equation:

     $x^2 + 2xy = 3y + 4$ $2xy - \text{.....................} = 4 - \text{.....................}$

   (b) Square both sides of the equation:

     $T = 2\pi\sqrt{h}$ $T^2 = \text{.....................}$

   (c) Multiply throughout the equation by the term on the bottom line of the fraction:

     $B = \dfrac{3C + 2}{5B} + 2C^2$ $\text{.....................} = 3C + 2 + \text{.....................}$

2 Complete the rearrangement of this formula, making n the subject, by filling in the blanks:

$$2n = 3m + \frac{5(2m - n)}{3k}$$

   Step 1 — Multiply the equation by $3k$:   ....

   Step 2 — Multiply out any brackets: ....

   Step 3 — Collect terms involving n on the left: ....

   Step 4 — .... $n(\text{..................}) = \text{................................}$

   Step 5 — Make n the subject: $n = \text{................................}$

3 Rearrange these formulas to make the letter in the brackets the subject:

   (a) $s = \dfrac{1}{2}gt^2$ (t) ....

   (b) $a + y = \dfrac{b - y}{a}$ (y) ....

   (c) $x = \sqrt{\dfrac{(1+n)}{(1-n)}}$ (n) ....

Inequalities

1   Complete the table of inequalities for the INTEGER values of x, y, z and p.

Statement	Inequality	Possible values
x is between -3 and $+5$, but never equal to either number	$-3 < x < 5$	
	$2 < y < 8$	
		$-5, -4, -3, -2, -1, 0$
	$p^2 < 16$	

2   Solve the following inequalities:

(a) $3x \leq 5 + 2x$ ....

(b) $10 < 2x - 6$ ....

(c) $4x + 1 > x - 5$ ....

(d) $\dfrac{2x}{5} \leq 3$ ....

3

(a) Find the integer values p which satisfy the inequality $9 < 2p \leq 18$.

....

(b) Solve the inequality $4q - 5 < 23$

....

(c) Solve the inequality $2r - 2 \geq 4r + 5$

....

Inequalities

1   Solve these double inequalities. Treat each side as a separate inequality.

   (a) $10 \leq 2x \leq x + 9$

   ....

   ....

   (b) $3 < 3x - 1 < 2x + 7$

   ....

   ....

   (c) $4x + 1 < 5x < 3(x + 2)$

   ....

   ....

2   The shaded region R is bounded by the lines
   $y = 2$, $y = x$ and $x + y = 8$.
   Write down three inequalities which define R.

   ....

   ....

   ....

3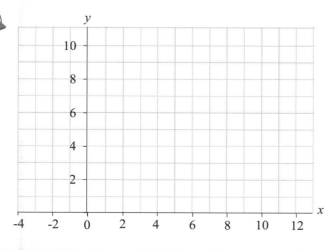

   (a) Use the grid to draw the graphs of
        $2x + y = 10$ and $y = x + 2$.

   (b) Shade and label, using the letter S, the
        area represented by the inequalities

        $x \geq 0$, $2x + y \leq 10$, $y \geq x + 2$

Factorising Quadratics

1 Use expressions from the box to factorise the quadratics below.

$2x + 3$	$x - 5$	$2x - 5$	$x + 3$	$2x + 5$	$x + 5$

(a) $2x^2 - 7x - 15 = ($............................$)($............................$)$

(b) $4x^2 - 25 = ($............................$)($............................$)$

(c) $x^2 + 8x + 15 = ($............................$)($............................$)$

2 **Solve** these quadratic equations by factorising:

(a) $x^2 + 9x + 20 = 0$ ....

....

(b) $3x^2 - 4x - 4 = 0$ ....

....

(c) $2x^2 + x - 28 = 0$ ....

....

(d) $m^2 - 4m = 0$ ....

....

3 Rearrange and solve these quadratic equations:

(a) $x^2 = 15 - 2x$ ....

....

(b) $4y + 5 = y^2$ ....

....

(c) $12 = 3x^2 - 5x$ ....

....

The Quadratic Formula

1 The 'quadratic formula' can be used to solve equations of the form $ax^2 + bx + c = 0$.
Write down the values of a, b and c in the equations below:

(a) $x^2 + 2x - 5 = 0$ $a =$ .... $b =$ .... $c =$ ....

(b) $2x^2 - 5x + 1 = 0$ $a =$ .... $b =$ .... $c =$ ....

(c) $5x^2 - 7x - 2 = 0$ $a =$ .... $b =$ .... $c =$ ....

2 The expression $b^2 - 4ac$ can be used to determine how many solutions a
quadratic equation $ax^2 + bx + c = 0$ has.

(a) Explain why there will be no solutions if $b^2 - 4ac < 0$.

....

....

(b) Determine whether the following quadratic equations have any solutions:

(i) $x^2 - 3x + 4 = 0$ ....

(ii) $2x^2 + 4x = 7$ ....

3 Solve these quadratic equations. Give your answers to 3 decimal places.

(a) $x^2 + 5x + 3 = 0$ ....

....

....

(b) $2x^2 - 7x = -2$ ....

....

....

(c) $3x^2 - 2x = 4$ ....

....

....

Completing the Square

1 Choose a bracket and a number from the box to complete the square for each quadratic equation below.

Brackets:	$(x + 5)$	$(x + 4)$	$(x + 3)$	$(x - 1)$
Numbers:	26	19	4	2

(a) $x^2 + 8x - 3 =$ ....^{2} − .... $= 0$

(b) $x^2 + 6x + 7 =$ ....^{2} − .... $= 0$

(c) $x^2 + 10x - 1 =$ ....^{2} − .... $= 0$

(d) $x^2 - 2x - 3 =$ ....^{2} − .... $= 0$

2 Express each of the following as a completed square:

(a) $x^2 - 6x - 4 = 0$ ....

....

(b) $2x^2 + 12x + 14 = 0$ ....

....

3 Solve these quadratic equations by completing the square:

(a) $x^2 + 4x - 5 = 0$

....

....

(b) $x^2 - 3x = 3$ ....

....

....

(c) $3x^2 + 12x - 9 = 0$

....

....

Trial and Improvement

1. The equation $x^2(x + 1) = 56$ has a solution between $x = 3$ and $x = 4$, as shown below.
   When $x = 3$, $x^2(x + 1) = 3^2(3 + 1) = 36$ (too small)
   When $x = 4$, $x^2(x + 1) = 4^2(4 + 1) = 80$ (too big)

   (a) Calculate the following:

   $3.3^2(3.3 + 1) =$ ....

   $3.4^2(3.4 + 1) =$ ....

   $3.5^2(3.5 + 1) =$ ....

   $3.6^2(3.6 + 1) =$ ....

   $3.7^2(3.7 + 1) =$ ....

   (b) Using your calculations from part (a), determine the solution of $x^2(x + 1) = 56$,
   correct to 1 decimal place.

   ....

2. Use trial and improvement to solve these problems to the degree of accuracy stated:

   (a) The area of a rectangle is $h(h - 1) = 75$ cm^2, where h is between 9 cm and 10 cm.
   Find h correct to 1 decimal place.

   ....

   ....

   ....

   ....

   ....

   (b) The equation $y = x^3 - 5$ crosses the x-axis between $x = 1$ and $x = 2$. In other words, the
   solution of $x^3 - 5 = 0$ is between 1 and 2. Find the value of x correct to 2 decimal places.

   ....

   ....

   ....

   ....

   ....

Simultaneous Equations

1   Solve these pairs of simultaneous equations:

   (a) $x + 3y = 6$ $3x + y = 3$

   ....

   ....

   ....

   (b) $3x^2 = y + 5$ $y - x = 2$ (Give your answers to 2 decimal places.)

   ....

   ....

   ....

2   Follow the instructions to solve the sets of simultaneous equations:

   (a) $x^2 + y = 4$ and $y = 4x - 1$

   (i)   Form a quadratic in x by substituting for y.

   ....

   (ii) Solve your quadratic equation to find two values of x.

   ....

   ....

   (iii) Find the corresponding values of y.

   ....

   (b) $x^2 + y = 2$ and $y = 4x + 5$

   (i)   Form a quadratic in x by substituting for y:

   ....

   (ii) Solve your quadratic equation to find two values of x.

   ....

   ....

   (iii) Find the corresponding values of y.

   ....

Direct and Inverse Proportion

1   This question is about quantities that are directly and inversely proportional to each other.

(a) The quantities A and B are directly proportional. Complete the table of values.

A	3	6			81	
B	5		20	30		65

(b) P is inversely proportional to Q. Complete the table of values.

P	5	10		2		
Q	20		4		40	200

2   The cost of petrol is directly proportional to the quantity bought.

(a) If 9 litres costs £8.73:

   (i) How much does 1 litre cost? ....

   (ii) How much does 20 litres cost? ....

(b) Use the same method to find the mass of 9 cm of wire given that 15 cm has a mass of 19 g.

   ....

(c) A train travels 80 km in 100 minutes.

   (i) At the same speed, how long does it take to travel 1 km?

   ....

   (ii) How far will it travel in 2 hours 30 minutes?

   ....

3 Work out the answers to these inverse proportion questions:

(a) The time it takes to harvest the crop in a field is inversely proportional to the number of people working on it.

   If 12 people take 3 hours to complete the harvest, how long will it take 9 people?

   ....

(b) Find the time taken by 10 machines to make the same quantity of gears that 8 machines can make in 5 hours.

   ....

(c) A ship has sufficient food to cater for 250 passengers for 6 days.

   (i) For how many days can it cater for 300 passengers? ....

   (ii) How many passengers can it cater for on a 15-day cruise?

   ....

Variation

1 Complete these statements of proportionality. The first one has been done for you.

(a) $T = k\sqrt{W}$ T is ....*directly*.......... proportional to ......*the square root of W*......

(b) $A = kh^3$ A is .... proportional to ....

(c) $y = \dfrac{k}{x^2}$ y is .... proportional to ....

(d) $M = \dfrac{k}{\sqrt{d}}$ M is .... proportional to ....

2 Choose the correct value of k for each statement below from the box.

1.5	18	2.4	10

(a) b is proportional to h^2, and when $b = 90$, $h = 3$. $k =$ ....

(b) f is proportional to v^3, and when $f = 12$, $v = 2$. $k =$ ....

(c) x varies with the square root of y, and when $x = 12$, $y = 25$. $k =$ ....

(d) p is inversely proportional to r^2, and when $p = 2$, $r = 3$. $k =$ ....

3 Round a bend on a railway track the height difference (h) between the outer and inner rails must vary in direct proportion to the square of the maximum permitted speed (S).

(a) If $h = 35$ mm when $S = 50$ km/h, write an equation relating h and S.

....

....

(b) Calculate h when $S = 40$.

....

....

4 The value of y is inversely proportional to the cube of x. Also, $x = 8$ when $y = 1.5$. Find the value of y when $x = 2$.

....

....

....

Algebra Mini-Exam (1)

1 This question is about solving equations by completing the square.

   (a) Find the values of a and b such that:

$$x^2 - 6x + 4 = (x - a)^2 + b$$

....

....

   (b) Hence or otherwise solve the following equation. Leave your answer in the form $p \pm \sqrt{q}$.

$$2x^2 - 12x + 8 = 0$$

....

....

2 This question is about factorising and simplifying expressions.

   (a) Factorise completely:

     (i) $2y^3 + 4y^2$

....

     (ii) $y^2 - 4$

....

   (b) Hence, simplify the expression $\dfrac{2y^3 + 4y^2}{y^2 - 4}$.

....

3 Solve the equation $4(p + 1) + 3(2p - 7) = 8$.

....

....

4 Solve the inequality $-3 < 2(x + 1) < 5$.

....

....

....

Algebra Mini-Exam (1)

5 This question is about factorising and solving quadratic equations.

(a) Factorise the expression $2x^2 + x - 6$.

....

....

(b) Hence solve the equation $2x^2 + x - 6 = 0$.

....

....

6 Solve the simultaneous equations:

$$x^2 + y = 6$$
$$7x = 3 + 2y$$

Do **not** use a trial and improvement method.

....

....

....

....

7 D and H are both positive quantities. D is directly proportional to the square of H.
When $D = 12$, $H = 4$.

(a) Express D in terms of H.

....

....

(b) Calculate D when $H = 8$.

....

....

(c) Calculate H when $D = 3$.

....

....

Algebra Mini-Exam (2)

1 Solve the equation $\dfrac{2x+1}{5} + \dfrac{x+9}{4} = 1$. Give your answer to 2 d.p.

....

....

....

2 Solve the inequality $\dfrac{3x+1}{5} + 3 < 0$. Give your answer to 2 d.p.

....

....

3 Susie is using trial and improvement to find a solution to the equation $x^3 + 4x = 50$.
This table shows her first two tries:

x	$x^3 + 4x$	Comment
3	39	too small
4	80	too big

Continue the table to find a solution to the equation, correct to 2 decimal places.

Final answer: ....

4 Solve the quadratic equation $2x^2 - 3x - 7 = 0$.
Give your solution correct to 2 decimal places.

....

....

....

....

Algebra Mini-Exam (2)

5   Mr. Jones invests £5000 at an interest rate of 7% per annum.

(a) How much interest will he earn in the first year?

....

(b) Calculate the value of his savings after 5 years.

....

....

(c) How many years will it be before he doubles his money?

....

....

6   The quantity x is proportional to y^3.

(a) When $y = 5$, $x = 200$. Find the value of x when $y = 3$.

....

....

The quantity y is also inversely proportional to the square root of z.

(b) When $y = 10$, $z = 9$. Find the value of z when $y = 12$.

....

....

7   Simplify the following expressions:

(a) $\dfrac{x^3}{x^8}$ ....

(b) $\left(x^{3/2}\right)^2$ ....

(c) $\dfrac{x^5 \times x^{-3}}{x^4 \times x^{-2}}$ ....

8   A and B are two numbers in standard form. $A = 1.23 \times 10^3$, $B = 5.5 \times 10^{-2}$

Evaluate, giving your answers in standard form to 3 significant figures:

(a) $A \times B$ .... (b) $B \div A$ ....

(c) $A \div B$ .... (d) B^2 ....